CYCLES

Alma Whitney

Senior Authors
Carl B. Smith
Ronald Wardhaugh

Literature Consultant
James E. Higgins
Skills Consultant
Larry A. Harris

Macmillan Publishing Co., Inc.
New York
Collier Macmillan Publishers
London

Macmillan Publishing Co., Inc.
866 Third Avenue, New York, N.Y. 10022
Collier-Macmillan Canada, Ltd.

Printed in the United States of America ISBN 0-02-123100-1   2-Q

ACKNOWLEDGMENTS

Editor: *Mary Keller*

Art Direction: *Zlata Paces*

Cover Design: *Norman Gorbaty Design, Inc.* Illustrators: Ray Cruz, p. 4-5; Lynn Sweat, p. 6-7; Irving Cohen, p. 8-11; Sal Murdocca, p. 12; Robert Jackson, p. 13; Lowren West, p. 16-17; Jackie Geyer, p. 18-28; Arthur Friedman, p. 30-38; Vladimir Fuka Hervert, p. 40-51; Richard Rosenblum, p. 52-57; Roberto Innocenti, p. 58; Angela Adams, p. 60-75; Joan Thompson, p. 76-78; Tony Chen, p. 80-84.

Photo credits: Dr. E. R. Degginger, pp. 14-17; James Foote, pp. 85-92; Tom McHugh from Photo Researchers. (photo) p. 90.

The publisher gratefully acknowledges permission to reprint the following copyrighted material:

"Baby Chick" reprinted from *Runny Days, Sunny Days* by Aileen Fisher. Copyrighted 1933, 1938, 1946, © 1958 by Aileen Fisher. By permission of Abelard Schumann, Ltd., an Intext publisher.

"The Inside Story of the Egg" by Edward Schano appeared in the May/June 1971 issue of *Ranger Rick's Nature Magazine*, and is reprinted by permission of the author.

"The Enormous Egg" adapted from *The Enormous Egg* by Oliver Butterworth. Copyright © 1956 by Oliver Butterworth. Reprinted by permission of Atlantic-Little Brown and Co.

"The City Under the Back Steps" from *The City Under the Back Steps* by Evelyn Lampman. Copyright © 1960 by Evelyn Sibley Lampman. Reprinted by permission of Doubleday & Company, Inc., and Faber and Faber, Ltd.

"Anteater" from *Boy Blue's Book of Beasts* by William Jay Smith. Copyright © 1957 by William Jay Smith. Reprinted by permission of the author.

"The Carp in the Bathtub" adapted from *The Carp in the Bathtub* by Barbara Cohen. Copyright © 1972 by Barbara Cohen. By permission of Lothrop, Lee and Shepard Company, Inc.

"Food Chains" from *The Links of Life: Food Chains* by Robert Gray appeared in the January 1972 issue of *Ranger Rick's Nature Magazine*. Reprinted by permission of the publisher, The National Wildlife Federation.

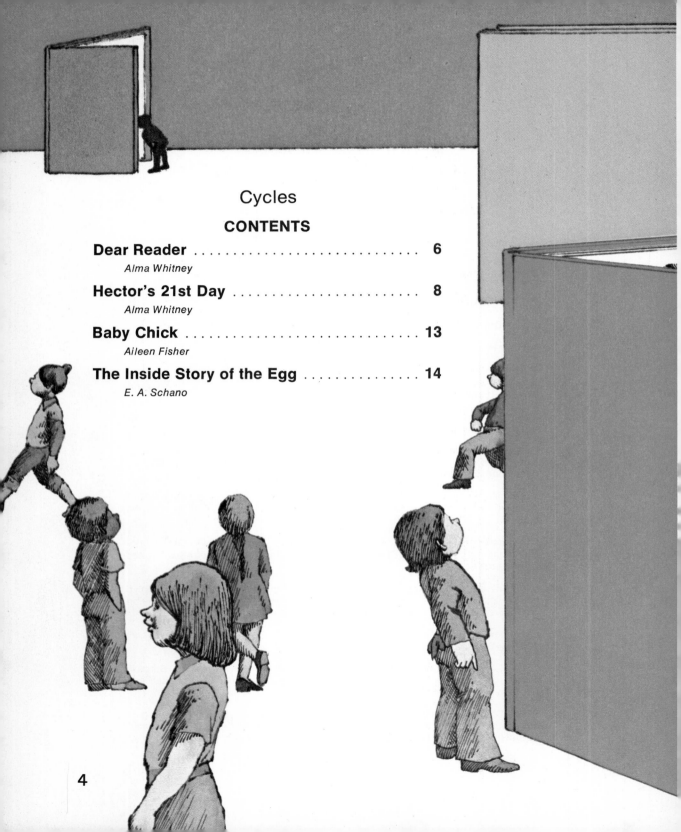

Cycles

CONTENTS

Dear Reader:

This book is about science. One reason we study science is to find out about the world around us. Our world is full of all kinds of wonderful and strange living things. And all of these living things, no matter how large or how small, depend on each other to live.

The scientist is an investigator of our world. In the search for ways to understand and improve the world, the scientist may study the way a chick develops inside an egg. Or, the scientist may look at how living things are related, through food chains, for example. But no matter what the scientist is investigating, the same process is always followed. The scientist collects facts and sorts them out. And then the scientist uses them to improve old ideas and build new ones.

In this book, you'll read about many boys and girls who are also investigating their world. One boy is keeping charts on his most unusual pet. Another boy and girl are researching the reasons for the disappearance of the dinosaurs. And all the boys and girls in a class are trying to find out what they can do to save animals that are in danger of becoming extinct.

All of these people have something in common. They are all trying to understand their world. As you read, you may think of things you would like to investigate. And you may get ideas about how you, too, can help make our world a better place.

Alma Whitney

HECTOR'S 21st DAY

Alma Whitney

After twenty-one days of being inside, it was time for Hector to get out. Getting out was not going to be easy. Not with a wall all around him. But enough was enough. Hector had to get out!

At first, Hector tried kicking his way out. But he could hardly move his legs. They were curled tightly under him. And he was jammed right up against the wall. He was crowded into a very small space.

The only thing that Hector could move was his head. But how in the world could he use his head to break down a wall? He needed something sharp, something with a point that could make a hole. Why, of course! He could use his tooth, his one and only tooth, as a tool. Hector had never used his tooth before. He hadn't needed it for eating. The food in his big yellow food bag had gotten to him through a tube in his tummy. But now his tooth was going to come in very handy.

Hector pulled his head back a little. Then he pushed his tooth against the wall as hard as he could. Push, push, push . . . nothing. Nothing happened. Hector tried again. Push, push, push . . . still nothing. Hector was not very happy about the way things were working out.

"If only it weren't so crowded in here," he thought, "then maybe I could just stay put." But the more he thought about it, the more he was sure that he could not stay where he was. Not only was it crowded, but his big yellow bag of food was gone. He would starve to death if he didn't make his move pretty soon.

Hector went to work again. He pulled his head back as far as it would go and struck at the wall with his tooth. Again and again he hit the wall. And again and again nothing happened. But just as Hector was about to give up, something exciting happened. As he hit the wall with his tooth, there was a slight sound...

Hector could hardly believe it. Right in the spot where he had been working was the tiniest of cracks. The wall had a crack in it. He was making progress!

Hector was thrilled. But as excited as he was, Hector was also very tired. This was hard work, indeed. Hector closed his eyes and took a nap. Not a long one, though. In a short time, he was at work again, jamming his only tooth in the crack in the wall.

How proud Hector must have been as he went about his job! Just think. Twenty-one days ago he had hardly been anything at all. In fact, he had looked like just a little white spot in the beginning. But by the time he had been around for three days, he had a head and a heart pumping blood. And after six days, he had eyes. In three more days, Hector had the beginnings of legs and the beginnings of wings. Then after ten days, his beak had started to form. And that tooth. Let's see. Oh, yes. That had formed on Hector's beak by the time he had been around for about twelve days.

Hector worked busily at the wall. He rammed his tooth against it again and again. And each time he did, the crack got a little bigger. Suddenly there was a sound much louder than the crack Hector had heard before...

CRUUUUNCH..

There was no longer just a crack in the wall. Now there was a little hole. Little, but big enough for Hector to stick his tooth through. And that is just what Hector did. He stuck his tooth through the hole in the wall and made as much noise as he could.

All that noise-making. All that work. Time for another nap. Hector pulled his tooth back inside. He fell asleep.

A little while later, Hector woke with a start. There was still a lot of work to be done. He pushed his tooth against the crack in the wall. The crack got bigger and bigger with each push. Time passed.

The crack in the wall went almost all the way around Hector now. Seeing this, Hector tried again to kick his way out.

He pushed his feet as hard as he could. Not yet. It wasn't quite time yet. He tried again. Kick, kick, kick . . .

With a loud noise, the wall finally split open.

Hector was so excited that he started making more noise than before. But he was not out yet. Hector still had a little squirming and wiggling to do before he would really be free.

So he squirmed. And he wiggled. And he wiggled and squirmed. And he pushed his feet with all his might against the wall. And then . . .

HECTOR WAS FINALLY OUT!

Did he leap for joy? Did he run around yelling about what a good job he had done? No, he did not. He simply wobbled around a little bit. And then he fell asleep.

It would take a little while before Hector's wet, flattened-out feathers would look dry and fluffy. It would take some time before Hector would be rested enough to walk about properly. But he really didn't care about that now. He was just glad he was out of the shell and on his way to being a lively little chick.

BABY CHICK

Peck
  peck
   peck
on the warm brown egg.
Out comes a neck.
Out comes a leg.
How
  does
   a chick,
who's not been about,
discover the trick
of how to get out?

—*Aileen Fisher*

the inside story of the egg

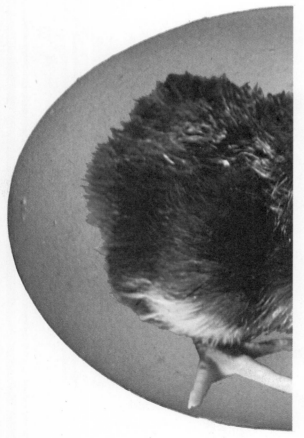

All female birds lay eggs. Ostriches lay very big eggs. Hummingbirds lay very small ones. Hens lay up to 350 eggs a year. But some birds lay only one egg a year.

Bird eggs come in all sizes and colors. They may look different on the outside. But on the inside, bird eggs are very much alike.

In all eggs that will hatch, the bird-to-be starts out as only a tiny,

E. A. Schano

whitish spot. All eggs contain a yellow part called the yolk. The yolk and the white of the egg give food to the bird-to-be as it is growing inside the egg. The yolk and the white of the egg are a cushion for the bird-to-be. The shell of the egg protects the bird-to-be until it is ready to hatch.

You have just read about a chick hatching out of its shell. Now let's take a look at how the chick looks as it grows inside the egg.

1

FIRST DAY: Can you see the whitish spot in this picture of the yolk of an egg? This is the beginning of a new chick.

3

THREE DAYS: The chick-to-be now looks like a question mark. It already has a heart. Do you see the little red lines all around the chick-to-be? These are blood vessels that carry blood and food to the chick-to-be.

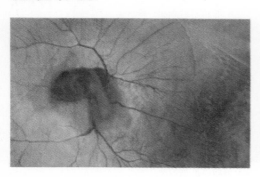

6

SIX DAYS: You can now see the eyes of the chick-to-be.

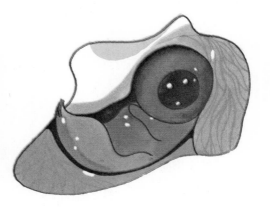

9

NINE DAYS: The wings and the tail are beginning to form. Can you see the little bumps on the body? These bumps are where feathers will grow.

12

TWELVE DAYS: Now the feathers are beginning to come out. The beak has already formed. Look carefully. Find the little tooth. This tooth will help the chick-to-be to hatch. The tooth will fall off soon after the chick is out of the shell.

That will give the new chick enough food to last for two or three days after it is hatched.

21

TWENTY-ONE DAYS: And here it comes! The chick-to-be has a strong neck. This helps the chick-to-be to hit its tooth against the shell. The chick-to-be does this for many hours. Finally the shell breaks open.

18

EIGHTEEN DAYS: Now the little chick-to-be almost fills up the egg. The yolk of the egg is getting watery. This is because the chick-to-be has been using it for food. Soon the chick-to-be will use up the whole yolk.

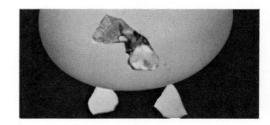

THE ENORMOUS EGG

Oliver Butterworth

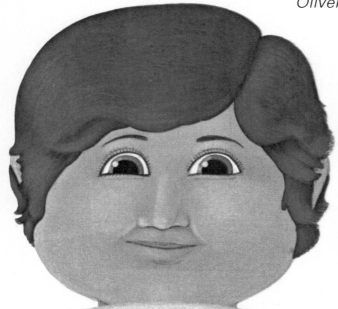

Sometimes
writers like to mix real things with
things that have never happened. For example,
we all know that chickens lay eggs that hatch into
chicks. Now think of all the other creatures that lay eggs.
Suppose things got mixed up and a chicken laid an egg that
hatched into a different animal. And suppose this animal was
believed to be extinct. What do you think would happen?
Oliver Butterworth thought about what it would be like if
this happened. And he wrote all about it in his book
called The Enormous Egg.

The day the egg hatched, I saw Joe Champigny out in his backyard. I went over to talk to him.

"Hey, Joe," I said. "Guess what hatched out of my egg?"

"A duck?" Joe asked.

"Nope."

"A turkey?"

"Nope. I'll give you a hint. It's got four legs."

Joe looked at me and wrinkled his face. "Two ducks?"

I could see that he wasn't going to get anywhere that way. So I told him. "It's a *dinosaur*. A real little live dinosaur. What do you think of *that*?"

"Aw, go on," Joe said. "Who are you kidding?"

"*Honest,* it is. Come on over and look at it. It's got little horns on its face and everything." We went across the street into my backyard. We squatted down by the dinosaur nest. Joe didn't see him at first. But then his eyes got used to the dark. "Jeepers, it's a big lizard!" he said. "Is he poisonous? He sure looks poisonous to me."

"I don't know," I said. I hadn't even thought of that before. I'd have to ask Dr. Ziemer.

"That's no dinosaur," Joe Champigny said. "It's just a big lizard. Where'd you get the idea it was a dinosaur, anyway?"

"Dr. Ziemer said it was one. Dr. Ziemer works in a museum. He knows all about dinosaurs and things like that. He knew the egg was going to hatch out. And he knew what kind of an egg it was, too."

"You know what I think?" Joe said. "This Dr. Ziemer is just making fun of you."

I didn't agree with what Joe said about Dr. Ziemer. He didn't look like the kind of man who'd play a trick like that. And he looked too excited when he first saw what had hatched out of the egg.

That afternoon, Dr. Ziemer drove up in his car. He walked out to the backyard, where I was sitting watching the dinosaur.

"Hello there, Nate," he said. "How is our little freak? Still lively?" He bent down and looked inside the box to make sure for himself. "Yes sir, he looks fine. Probably hungry, too."

"What does he eat?" I said. "Do we have to feed him milk out of a baby's bottle?"

Dr. Ziemer laughed at that. "Oh no, Nate. You see, dinosaurs are reptiles like snakes and turtles. When they hatch out of the egg, they are all ready to eat the same kind of food that grown-up dinosaurs eat. Your dinosaur is a *Triceratops*. The *Triceratops* kind of dinosaur is a grass-eater. So all we have to do is keep him supplied with grass or leaves or lily pads or lettuce—and a few small pebbles now and then."

"Pebbles?" I said. "Does he eat pebbles?"

Dr. Ziemer smiled. "What kind of teeth does a chicken have, Nate?"

"Doesn't have teeth," I said. "It just has little stones in its gizzard. Say, do you mean a dinosaur has a gizzard like a chicken?"

"Some of them do. When scientists dug up dinosaur bones, they sometimes found a pile of smooth stones right in the middle of the dinosaur skeleton. They finally figured out that they were gizzard stones. Some of the stones were as big as a man's fist."

We picked some maple leaves from the tree in the yard. And I got a handful of grass from outside the fence. We put them down in two piles—grass in one and leaves in the other. We put the nest box on its side. The dinosaur could come out if he wanted to. Then we sat down and watched. The little dinosaur saw the piles of food, I guess, because he started right out for them. His legs looked kind of weak at first. And he stumbled around a little. But he kept right on going. The first pile he came to was the grass. He put his head right down into

that green grass. He started swallowing away at it. The little fellow kept right on swallowing until the handful of grass was all gone. All that was left was a blade of grass hanging out of the corner of his mouth. Then he wobbled over to the pile of leaves. He started in on that. I ran over and got some more grass and another pile of leaves.

When it was all gone, he stood on three legs and scratched his neck with a hind foot. Then he walked over to a smooth, sunny place and lay down.

"Well," Dr. Ziemer said, "with that appetite he's going to have us jumping to keep him supplied with food. By the way, we ought to keep a record of his growth. Do you happen to have some scales in the house?"

We did. I brought the scales outside, and we put them on the ground. Then I went over to pick up the animal. He had a bluish skin like a lizard's. And he had a funny kind of a beak, something like a snapping turtle has. I wasn't scared to pick him up. But you see, I'd never handled a dinosaur before. And I didn't know much about how to do it.

Dr. Ziemer was watching me. "What's the matter, Nate? Does he look dangerous?"

"I was just wondering how I ought to get hold of him," I said. "He has a kind of sharp-looking mouth. I'd just as soon not get my hand nipped. What do you think?"

"Well, to tell the truth, I've never had to deal with any of these fellows when they were alive. My dinosaurs have all been just piles of old bones. Let's just see how touchy he is." He put his foot out and gently poked one of the dinosaur's feet. The dinosaur sat up and looked around. He was pretty sleepy.

"He looks rather calm and friendly," the doctor said. "Would you like me to pick him up this first time?"

As a matter of fact, I wasn't too eager to catch hold of him. But I thought I ought to be the one to pick him up first, since he was my dinosaur and all. So I said, "No thanks, I'll pick him up."

"All right, Nate. I'd suggest you hold him just back of the front legs. He has a short neck. I don't think he could reach you that way. Be easy, now. We don't want to frighten him."

I reached down slowly. I slid my hands around his body. He wriggled a little but didn't try to bite. His skin felt all warm and sort of slidy and loose. When he seemed to be used to my hands being there, I picked him up slowly and set him down on the scales.

We looked at the dial on the scales. It said four- and- a- quarter pounds. The doctor wrote that down in a little notebook.

"Of course," he said, " this is not what he weighed before he ate. Let's gather as much grass and leaves as we had before. Then we'll weigh that and see how much he's eaten."

We gathered the grass and leaves, and it weighed just a little over a pound.

"Your baby's got a good appetite," the doctor said. "The food he ate weighed over a third of his own weight. Let's see now, that means that he weighed about three pounds when he hatched." He wrote that down in his notebook. "And now for his length." He took a tape measure out of his pocket.

We stretched out his tail and measured him from tip to tip. He was thirteen−and−a−half inches. The doctor wrote it down. Then he measured his head and the length of his tail and his legs. He wrote the measurements down each time in his notebook.

"Is a *Tricerapops* poisonous, Dr. Ziemer?" I asked him.

"No sir, Nate. These fellows had too much armor to need poison. Do you think I'd ask you to pick him up if I thought he was poisonous?"

"How big does the *Tricerapops* get to be?" I asked.

"Sometimes more than twenty feet, with the tail, of course," said Dr. Zeimer. "And it's Tricera*tops*, not *pops*. They might weigh up to ten tons or so at full size."

"Ten tons!" I almost fell over backward with surprise. "My gosh, think of all the grass it would take to feed him. How long does it take him to get that big?"

"Oh, it would take a long time, I'm sure," said Dr. Ziemer. "The fact is, we don't really know much about how fast these animals grew. We've never had any live ones before. We know how big they were because we've found their skeletons. But we don't know much else about them. That's why we must keep careful records on this little fellow. Science is going to be very interested."

Dr. Ziemer finished writing and said he had to go into the house for a minute.

I sat down under the maple tree in the shade. Pretty soon Joe Champigny came along and sat down with me.

"How's your lizard, Nate?" he said.

"It's no lizard. It's a dinosaur."

"I betcha it isn't. I asked my pop about it. He said there wasn't any such thing as dinosaurs. Some crazy scientist found a lot of old bones and made up all that business about dinosaurs."

"There were too dinosaurs," I said. "Besides, if there weren't dinosaurs, how come I've got one right here?"

"Fooey, that's no dinosaur," Joe said.

"It is too. It's a *Triceraclops*, or something like that. And if a *Triceralcops* isn't a dinosaur, I'd like to know what *is*."

"Fooey," Joe Champigny said.

Sometimes Joe's an awfully hard guy to argue with.

What's in a Name?

Nate had some trouble remembering the name for his little lizard. If he had understood what the name meant, he probably would have had less trouble remembering it. Triceratops is an example of an animal name that is based on a special characteristic of the animal. Many of these names are made up of smaller Greek and Latin words. Once you know what these smaller words mean, you can figure out what the longer names mean.

For example, **tri** means "three." **Cerat** means "horn" and **ops** means "eye" or "face." When you put them all together, you get three-horned face, which is what a triceratops has.

Here are some more Greek and Latin words often used in naming animals:

rhinos . . . . nose		**porcus** . . . . **pig**
dino . . . . terrible		**ceros** . . . . horn
cent . . . . hundred		**saur** . . . . lizard
platy . . . . broad, flat		**pus** or **pede** . . foot
octo . . . . eight		**spina** . . . . spines

Now see if you can put these words together to name the animals shown below.

29

AND WHATEVER HAPPENED TO THE

TERRIBLE LIZARDS
ALMA WHITNEY

HERE IT IS, FRED. I'VE FOUND THE ANSWER. THIS BOOK SAYS:

SOME DINOSAURS ATE ONLY PLANTS. AS THE EARTH'S CLIMATE CHANGED, THESE PLANTS MAY HAVE DISAPPEARED. WHEN THE DINOSAURS COULD NOT FIND PLANTS TO EAT, THEY DIED FROM HUNGER. OTHER DINOSAURS WERE MEAT-EATERS. THEY ATE THE DINOSAURS WHO ATE PLANTS. WHEN THE PLANT-EATERS DIED, THE MEAT-EATERS HAD NOTHING TO EAT. SO THEY DIED, TOO.

ALL RIGHT, FRED, WHERE IS THAT POSTCARD?

JUST A MINUTE, MILLY. MY BOOK SAYS SOMETHING ELSE.

SOME DINOSAURS WERE AS SMALL AS CHICKENS. OTHERS WERE AS LONG AS FIVE CARS LINED UP END TO END AND AS TALL AS A TWO-STORY BUILDING. BUT ALL THE DINOSAURS HAD VERY SMALL BRAINS. THIS LEADS US TO BELIEVE THAT THE DINOSAURS WERE NOT VERY SMART. PERHAPS THAT IS WHY THEY BECAME EXTINCT. IT MAY BE THAT THEY WERE NOT SMART ENOUGH TO ESCAPE THEIR ENEMIES OR TAKE CARE OF THEMSELVES AS THE EARTH CHANGED.

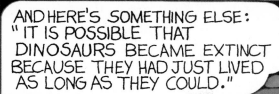

AND HERE'S SOMETHING ELSE: "IT IS POSSIBLE THAT DINOSAURS BECAME EXTINCT BECAUSE THEY HAD JUST LIVED AS LONG AS THEY COULD."

DO YOU THINK THAT'S POSSIBLE, FRED? DO YOU THINK THAT A WHOLE BUNCH OF ANIMALS COULD JUST BECOME EXTINCT BECAUSE THEY HAD LIVED LONG ENOUGH?

I REALLY DON'T KNOW, MILLY.

FRED, MAYBE THEY ALL JUST DIED BECAUSE OF SOME TERRIBLE SICKNESS.

THAT'S POSSIBLE. SICKNESSES HAVE KILLED OFF LOTS OF PEOPLE AT ONE TIME. MAYBE SOME TERRIBLE SICKNESS KILLED OFF THE DINOSAURS THE SAME WAY.

HOW ARE WE EVER GOING TO FIT ALL OF THIS ON ONE POSTCARD, FRED?

WELL, SINCE WE DON'T HAVE TIME TO WRITE A BOOK, WE COULD WRITE A LETTER.

35

Dinosaur Contest
The City Museum
1500 Center Street
Chicago, Illinois 60614

Dear Sirs:

Here's our answer to your question "Whatever Happened to the Terrible Lizards?" We can't fit it on a postcard, so we are writing you a letter.

1. Some dinosaurs ate plants. Maybe the plants disappeared and those dinosaurs starved. Some dinosaurs ate the dinosaurs that ate plants. When the plant-eaters died, the meat-eaters also died.

2. The dinosaurs were not very smart. Maybe they could not escape from their enemies or figure out how to take care of themselves as the earth changed.

3. Maybe the dinosaurs became extinct because smaller animals ate their eggs or because their eggs didn't hatch anymore.

4. Maybe the dinosaurs became extinct because they had just lived long enough.

5. Maybe the dinosaurs all got very sick and died. (That's our own idea.)

In other words, our answer is that no one knows for sure why dinosaurs became extinct.

Yours truly,
Milly and Fred

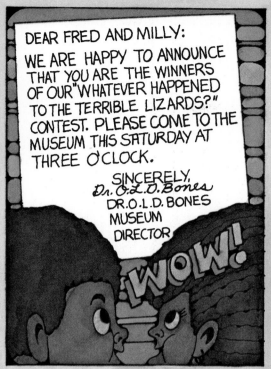

Group Names

A whole bunch of animals is one way of talking about a lot of animals. But there are special names for groups of some animals. Here are a few:

a school of fish **a pride of lions**

a swarm of bees **a flock of sheep or birds**

a gaggle of geese **a bevy of quail**

a herd of cows **a pack of wolves**

Some of these names describe something about the animals they name. The word **swarm** comes from an Old German word meaning "to whir or buzz." Bees do buzz. The word **flock** comes from the Old German word meaning "down" or "locks of wool." The soft feathers next to a bird's skin are called down. A sheep's body is covered with locks of wool. The word **school** comes from the Old English word meaning "a large group." Fish do travel in large groups.

You can have some fun thinking of names that would be suitable for other groups of animals or for people. For example, a peck of chickens. Find a word in the left-hand column below that would make a good name for each group of people in the right-hand column.

chain **carpenters**

kettle **bus drivers**

board **jewelers**

spatter **waiters**

spill **cooks**

drove **painters**

THE BIGGEST ANIMAL OF ALL...

Tyrannosaurus	Triceratops	Brachiosaurus
50 feet long	20 feet long	80 feet long
meat-eater	plant-eater	plant-eater

Brontosaurus
65 feet long
plant-eater

Stegosaurus
20 feet long
plant-eater

THE ANSWER IS YES!

Whales are the largest animals that have ever lived. The blue whale is the biggest whale of all. Some blue whales weigh as much as one hundred tons. A bus weighs about fifteen tons.

Some blue whales are nearly one
hundred feet long. A bus is
only about forty-five feet long.
The largest blue whales weigh
twice as much as a Brachiosaurus,
the heaviest of all the dinosaurs.

The City Under the Back Steps

Evelyn Lampman

Ants live in complete cities that they build under the ground. Each ant in an ant city has a special job to do. <u>The City Under the Back Steps</u> is a book about two children who shrink to the size of ants. They visit an ant city.

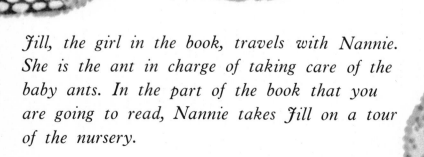

Jill, the girl in the book, travels with Nannie. She is the ant in charge of taking care of the baby ants. In the part of the book that you are going to read, Nannie takes Jill on a tour of the nursery.

Jill turned. She looked around the room. She wondered where the baby ants were kept. She could not see any. Along one wall was a stack of tiny white eggs. The eggs were piled in neat rows. The smaller ones were at one end. And the larger ones were at the other end. Some ants moved up and down in front of the row, licking each egg with their quick black tongues.

"Babies have to eat," Nannie said. "They are always hungry."

"That's what I've always heard," Jill agreed. "And they have to be kept clean, too. I guess that's what those nurses are doing over there — washing the eggs."

"Dear me, no," said Nannie. "Those eggs are clean. They are being fed. Come along. I'll show you. These are the newest babies," said Nannie. And she pointed to the smallest eggs. "They were just laid today. And there, at the other end of the wall, are the older babies. They have had many days of feeding and have grown quite fat. They are almost ready to be hatched into little larvae."

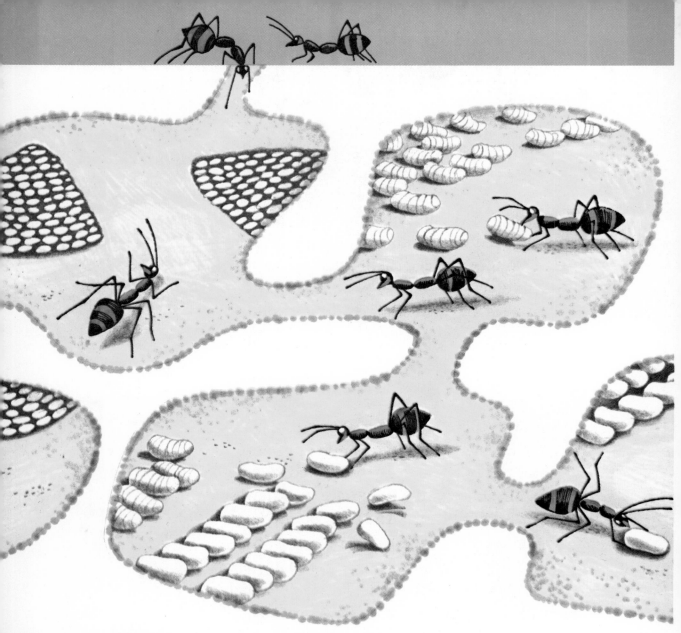

Jill did not want to say that she had never heard of eggs growing larger once they were laid or that she had no idea of what larvae were. So instead she asked, "What do the babies eat?" She had no idea about that either. There did not seem to be any bottles or food around.

"The babies have milk," said Nannie. "You really don't know anything about baby ants, do you?"

Nannie stopped talking. She moved her antennae. Then she turned to the other nurses in the room. "This room will soon be too chilly for the eggs. They must be moved to Nursery 7 at once."

"You have more than one nursery?"

"We have many of them," said Nannie. "We move things around all the time. The eggs must be kept at just the right temperature. And we move the eggs for safety, too. If we should be attacked by an enemy, the enemy would have to hunt for the nursery. Now come along. Let's go and see the babies who have already become larvae. They are in the next room."

There were so many larvae in the next room that Jill could not begin to count them. The larvae were also being licked by their nurses. Jill began to realize that the nurses had the baby food in their mouths. And she could see that by licking the eggs and larvae, the nurses were giving the food to the babies.

Jill did not want to say so, but she did not think the larva stage of ant babies was very pretty. The larvae looked like little, white, hairy worms. They were soft and squashy. And they did not have eyes. They had mouths, though. And out of their mouths came threads that looked like the webs a spider might spin. As Jill watched, the threads grew longer and longer. Nannie was excited when she saw them.

"Will you look at that," Nannie said. "Such smart babies. They are already changing into pupae!"

"Pupae," thought Jill. "My goodness. First the babies were eggs. Then the eggs turned to larvae. Then the larvae turned to something else. What a lot of steps there are before an ant becomes an ant!"

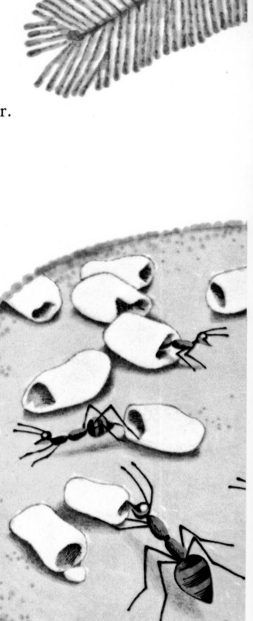

One of the wormlike creatures shook. Then it let out a long strand of thread. It rolled over and over until it was completely wrapped in the thread.

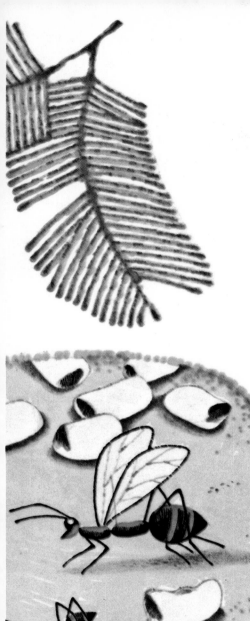

"Be careful," cried Jill. "It may choke."

"Bless your heart," said Nannie. "It's only doing what it's supposed to do. Soon it will spin enough thread so that it's wrapped up as neatly as a little sack. Then it will be a pupa. Come over here. You can see some."

The pupae did not have to be fed. In fact, it would have been impossible to feed them. The pupae were nothing but little cocoons of tightly wrapped thread. They were laid out in neat little rows. They looked like so many white packages. And there was no sign of the pale worm inside.

"Now it's time to go to the delivery room and see the new babies coming out of their pupae," Nannie said.

The delivery room was a busy place. It was not nearly as neat as the other rooms in the nursery. The cocoons were not piled in neat rows. They were lying here and there. The nurses were running about, trying to see everything at once.

Most of the cocoons were moving. Some only gave a little twitch or jerk. Others were tossing and jumping like little bits of popping corn. Here and there lay an empty pupa. And beside it lay a tiny dark insect. It looked like the larger ants but had a strange, soft body.

"Oh, there are the babies," cried Jill in excitement. "But they shouldn't be left on the floor. They might get cold."

"Don't touch them!" Nannie yelled. "They haven't been out of their cocoons long enough for their skins to harden. Give them a little while. Then it will be perfectly safe to hold them. Oh, here's one that's ready to come out but needs help."

Jill followed Nannie to one of the cocoons that was popping up and down. Nannie bent over the cocoon, holding it still with one of her feet. She opened her mouth and gently tore at the thread until there was room for the little ant to get out.

"Cute, isn't it?" Nannie said proudly. "We have to help them, poor dears. They have such a hard time getting started."

"Are they fed pretty soon?" Jill asked, staring at the newly hatched baby.

"Soon, but not here," said Nannie. "In a little while these babies will be strong enough to walk. Then they will be taken to another nursery to be washed and fed. They must not be touched until then."

"Now it's time to go," said Nannie. "We'll come back later."

"All right," said Jill. "But I hope all the babies won't be hatched by the time I get back."

"Don't worry about that," Nannie told her. "There are new babies every day. Our city must go on, you know."

Your Own Ant City

Lenore Flehinger

Reading about ants is one way to learn about them. Another way to learn about these interesting insects is by watching them. And what better way to watch them than in your own ant city?

Here is a plan for building an ant city and for keeping ants that you can do yourself.

BUILDING THE CITY

You will need:

Glass jar (at least quart size with a screw-on lid)

Piece of wood (as large as you can find that will fit into the jar)

Moist soil (the kind that holds together when you squeeze it)

Sponge

Black paper (enough to wrap around the jar)

String (two pieces long enough to tie around the jar)

Block of wood (to use as a stand for the jar)

Pan (large enough to hold the jar and the block of wood)

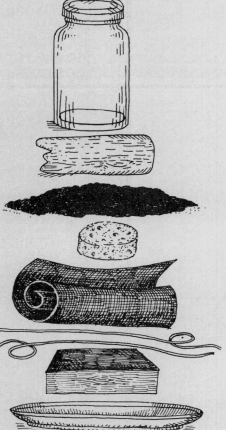

HOW TO PUT THE CITY TOGETHER

1. Stand the piece of wood in the center of the jar.

2. Fill in the space around the piece of wood with enough soil to hold the wood in place. (Ants make tunnels in their cities. If you do not put the wood in the jar, the ants might make their tunnels in the center of the jar. Then you would not be able to see them.)

3. Keep everything else ready until you bring your ants to their new home.

COLLECTING THE ANTS

You will need:

Glass jar
Old sheet or pillowcase
Small shovel or garden trowel

HOW TO FIND THE ANTS

Some ants make their homes under a stone or a rotting piece of wood. If the weather is warm, you may see many ants right under the stone or the wood. If the weather is cool, some ants may be where you can see them. But many others will be in their tunnels under the ground.

The first ants you'll see will be the workers. They gather food, care for the young, and even collect the garbage. Some of the workers will be carrying what look like grains of rice. They are really carrying the larvae, a stage of ant baby that you read about in <u>The City Under the Back Steps.</u> Gently dig out as many of the workers and the larvae as you can. Pile them, along with some of the soil you find them in, on the sheet or pillowcase. Then gently push as many workers as you can into the jar. You

will need about one hundred workers. If the workers drop the larvae, carefully push the larvae into the jar yourself. Be sure to put some of the soil from the nest into the jar also.

Finally, if you want your ant city to last for some time, you must have a queen ant. The queen is important because she lays the eggs from which new ants come. You can recognize the queen because she is bigger than the other ants. You may have to dig a bit and look very carefully to find her.

If you can't find ants under a rock or a piece of wood, look for an ant hill. An ant hill is a little cone of earth built around a tiny hole in the ground. If an ant nest is under an ant hill, you may have to dig quite deep to get the ants. But remember, you will need workers, larvae, and a queen to have a healthy city.

PUTTING THE ANTS IN THEIR NEW HOME

1. Bring the ants to their new home as quickly as you can. Put them, along with the soil you found them in, into the city you built.

2. Wet the sponge and wring it out well. Place it on top of the piece of wood in the jar. (This will keep the air in the jar from getting too dry.)

3. Wrap the black paper around the jar. Tie it with the two pieces of string. (Ants make their tunnels away from the light. If you do not cover the city, the ants will make their tunnels as close to the center of the jar as they can.)

4. Put water in the pan and set the block of wood in it. Then set your ant city on top of the block of wood. The ant city should not sit in the water, or the paper around it will get wet. (Ants will not go into water. If they try to get out of their city, the water will keep them from leaving.)

5. Punch some holes in the screw-on lid of the jar. Stuff the holes with cotton. (The cotton will let air in. But it will keep the ants from getting out.) Screw the cover on the jar.

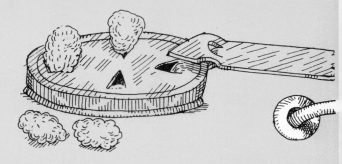

CARING FOR THE ANT CITY

You will need:

Eyedropper
Tweezers
Bits of food

WHAT TO DO

You must take care of your ant city every day. If it is in school, make sure you take good care of it during the week. Then it should be all right by itself on the weekends. Here are the things you should do to care for your ant city:

1. Check the sponge every day. See that it is moist. Add a drop or two of water from the eyedropper when the sponge starts to get dry.

2. Try to feed your ants at the same time each day. Put the food in the same place in their city. The ants will learn where and when to come and get the food. Ants especially like bread, cake, and sugar. You can also give them honey mixed with water. If you can find some dead insects, feed them to the ants, too. Put small pieces of food into the city every day. Each time you add new food, remove the old food with your tweezers. This keeps the city from getting moldy.

3. Leave the black paper tied around the ant city for the first few days after you put the ants in. After that, you may remove the paper for just a few minutes from time to time to look at your ants. By watching closely, you may be able to see the ants feed each other, care for the larvae, and collect the garbage. You may want to keep a diary of what you see.

Anteater

— William Jay Smith

The Anteater makes a meal of ants
That run up and down the leaves of plants.
No matter how hungry I ever got,
I wouldn't eat Ants, I would certainly not.
I think that Ants would make me squirm;
I'd rather eat an angleworm;
Or if it really came to that,
A mashed mosquito or a gnat,
But not a big red twitchety ant
That crawls on a fat green tropical plant.

58

Limericks

Limericks are funny verses. They always have the same number of lines—five. They always have the same form. The last words in the first two lines rhyme with the last word in the last line. The last words in lines three and four rhyme. Many limericks begin "There was a," but they don't have to. The last line of the limerick is usually a joke or some kind of funny ending. Read these limericks. Count the lines and check the rhymes.

There was a young lady from Roo
Who suddenly started to moo.
Her neighbors all tried
To take her inside.
Lest the cow say "How do you do?"

Now read these limericks.

You think of words that will fit in the blanks.

There was a young maid in
    fourth grade
Who was never, ever _____?_____.
A ghost she did meet
On a dark, quiet _____?_____.
And invited him home
    for orangeade.

A fellow who fell out of bed
Stood up and patted his _____?_____.
"I guess it's all right
But, oh, what a fright.
For a minute I thought I was _____?_____."

Now that you know how, write a limerick of your own.

(They make good presents for relatives.)

The Carp in the Bathtub

Barbara Cohen

When I was a little girl, I lived in an apartment house in New York City with Mama and Papa and my little brother Harry.

It was not very fancy, but Papa said we were lucky. We had our own bathroom. Mrs. Ginzburg, who lived downstairs, was also lucky. She had a bathroom, too. Everyone else had to share the bathrooms in the hall.

Mama was a wonderful cook. It was well known that she made the finest chicken soup in New York City. Everything she made was the best.

But best of all was Mama's gefilte fish. Mama made gefilte fish twice a year. She made it in the fall for the Jewish New Year. And she made it in the spring for the festival of Passover.

Everybody loved Mama's gefilte fish. But I will tell you a secret. I never put a piece of it into my mouth.

Mama made her gefilte fish out of carp. For a day or two before the holidays, carp was hard to find in the stores. All the ladies in the neighborhood had been buying it for their own gefilte fish. Mama liked to buy her carp at least a week early. She wanted to get the nicest, fattest, shiniest one. But Mama knew that a dead fish sitting in the icebox for a week would not be very good when the time came to make it into gefilte fish.

So Mama bought her fish live and carried it home in a pail of water. All the way home the fish flopped and flipped because it was too big for the bucket. It would have died if Mama had left it in there.

As soon as she got home, she would call, "Leah, run the water in the tub."

And I would put the rubber stopper in the drain and run some cold water into the bathtub. Then Mama would dump the carp out of the pail and into the tub.

The carp loved it there. He was always a big fish. But the tub was about four times as long as he was. And there was plenty of room for him to swim around.

Harry and I loved the carp. As long as he was there, we didn't have to take baths.

Most of our friends took baths only once a week. But because we had our own tub, Mama made us bathe twice a week.

"Otherwise," she said, "what is the use of having our own bathroom?"

We didn't think it was fair. And we would gladly have moved into an apartment where the tenants shared the bathrooms in the hall.

Except, of course, when we had a carp living in our bathtub. Harry and I would go into the bathroom and feed the carp a rusty lettuce leaf or a crust of bread.

But the day always came when Mama marched into the bathroom and took the stopper out of the tub. The carp always seemed to know what was coming. He swam away from her as fast as he could, splashing water all over her apron with his strong, flat tail. But he didn't even have a chance. Before all the water was out of the tub, Mama had caught the carp. Then she dumped him right into the bucket and carried him to the kitchen.

We knew what she did with him when she got there, although we would never look. She killed him. Then she scraped off the scales with a huge knife. The head, skin, and bones she boiled, along with some carrots and onions, in a big kettle of water to make broth. She put the meat through a meat grinder with some more onions. After she put in some other things, she made the mixture into balls. She took the broth and put it through a strainer to remove all the skin and bones, which she threw into the garbage.

Mama saved the broth for cooking the fish balls. That took hours. Harry and I would run out into the hall. But even there we could not escape the smell of fish.

Mama once told us that her mama had not thrown away the fish skin. She removed it carefully from the carp. After the fish was cooked, she could put it back in the skin and bring it to the table. That's why the fish is called *gefilte*. Mama said, "*Gefilte* means stuffed." At least Harry and I never had to see that!

You can see why we managed never to eat gefilte fish on the Jewish New Year or Passover. Could *you* eat a friend?

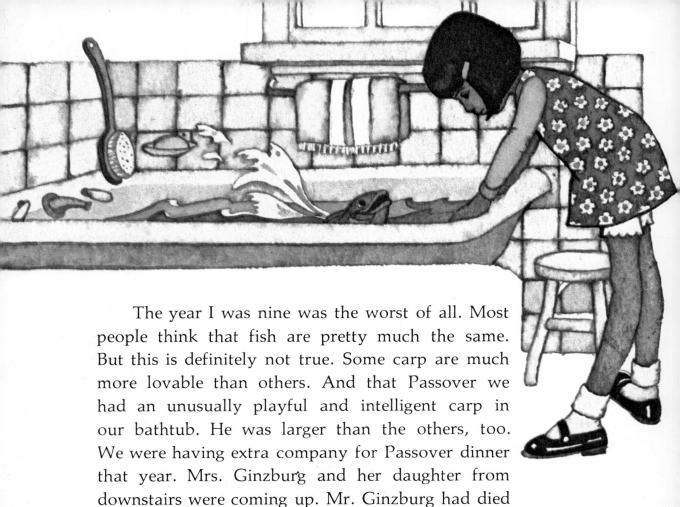

The year I was nine was the worst of all. Most people think that fish are pretty much the same. But this is definitely not true. Some carp are much more lovable than others. And that Passover we had an unusually playful and intelligent carp in our bathtub. He was larger than the others, too. We were having extra company for Passover dinner that year. Mrs. Ginzburg and her daughter from downstairs were coming up. Mr. Ginzburg had died six months before. And Mrs. Ginzburg didn't have the heart to fuss over Passover.

This carp was also shinier than the others. His eyes were brighter. And he seemed much livelier and friendlier. It got so that whenever Harry or I went into the bathroom, he'd swim right over to the end of the tub nearest to us as if he knew we were going to feed him. There was something about his mouth that made him seem to be smiling at us after he had eaten his bread crust or his lettuce.

In those days, people like us did not have pets. Harry and I would have loved owning a dog, a cat, or a bird. But Mama and Papa had never thought of such a thing. And we never thought to ask. I'll tell you one thing, though. After that carp had been in our bathtub for nearly a week, we knew he was not just any old carp. He was our pet. In memory of Mr. Ginzburg, we called him Joe.

Two days before Passover, when I came home from school, Mama said, "You look after Harry, Leah. I have to go out. I'll never get anything done if I have him trailing after me."

As soon as Mama was gone, I looked at Harry, and Harry looked at me.

"We have to save Joe," I told him.

"We'll never have another chance," Harry agreed. "But what'll we do?"

"Mrs. Ginzburg has a bathtub," I reminded him.

Harry nodded. He saw what I meant right away.

I went into the kitchen, got the bucket, and carried it to the bathroom. Harry had already let the water out of the tub. He helped lift Joe into the bucket. It was not easy for us because Joe must have weighed fifteen pounds. But we finally managed. We could add only a little water to the pail because it was already almost too heavy for us.

With both of us holding onto the handle and banging the bucket against every step, we lugged Joe downstairs to Mrs. Ginzburg's door. Then we rang her bell. It took her a long time to get to the door. But she finally opened it.

"Why, Leah, Harry!" she said in surprise. "I'm very glad to see you. Won't you come in? Why are you carrying that bucket?" Mrs. Ginzburg was a very nice lady. She was always kind to us, even when she couldn't understand what we were doing.

We carried our bucket into Mrs. Ginzburg's front room. "May I ask what you have there?" she said politely.

"It's Joe," said Harry.

"Joe!" Mrs. Ginzburg closed her eyes and put her hand over her heart.

"We named him for Mr. Ginzburg," I explained quickly. "He smiles like Mr. Ginzburg."

"Oh..." Mrs. Ginzburg tried to smile, too. Just then Joe twitched. His tail flashed over the top of the bucket. And a few drops of water dripped onto Mrs. Ginzburg's rug. Mrs. Ginzburg glanced into the pail. "My goodness," she said, "he looks like a fish to me."

"He is a fish," I said. "He's the best fish in the world, and Mama can't kill him for Passover. She just can't. Please let him stay in your bathtub. Please. Just for a little while. Until I can figure out where to keep him for good."

"But, Leah," Mrs. Ginzburg said, "I can't do that. Your mama is my dear friend."

"If you don't let us put Joe in your bathtub soon," Harry pleaded, "he'll be dead. He's almost dead now."

Mrs. Ginzburg and I peered into the bucket. Harry was right. Joe didn't look too good. His scales weren't shiny bright anymore, and he had stopped thrashing around. There was not enough water in the bucket for him.

"All right," said Mrs. Ginzburg. "But just for now." She ran some water into her tub, and we dumped our carp in. He no sooner felt all that clear cold water around him than he perked right up and started swimming. I took a few morsels of chopped meat I had stored away in my dress pocket and gave them to him. He smiled at me, just like always.

"This fish can't stay here," Mrs. Ginzburg warned. "I'm afraid I can't help hide him from your mother and father."

"What shall we do?" Harry asked me, blinking his eyes hard to keep back the tears.

"We'll go find Papa," I told him. "Papa doesn't cook, so maybe he'll understand. We'll have to find him before Mama gets home."

Every night, Papa came home on the subway from his job in a factory. That night, Harry and I went down to the corner and waited by the stairs that led up from the station. After a while, we saw a big crowd of people who had just gotten off the train come up the stairs. Papa was with them. He

was holding onto the rail and climbing slowly, with his head down.

"Papa, Papa," we called.

He looked up and saw us. He straightened his shoulders, smiled, and ran quickly up the few remaining steps.

"You came to meet me," he said. "That's very nice."

We started home together. I was holding one of Papa's hands, and Harry was holding the other. "Papa," I asked, "do you like gefilte fish?"

"Why, yes," he said, "of course I like gefilte fish. Your mother makes the best gefilte fish in all of New York."

"But would you eat gefilte fish," Harry asked, "if the fish was a friend of yours?"

Papa stood absolutely still right in the middle of the sidewalk. "Harry," he said, "Harry, what have you done to Mama's fish?"

"Leah did it, too," Harry said.

Papa turned to me. Putting his hands on my shoulders, he looked right into my eyes. Papa's brown eyes were not large. But they were very bright. Most of the time his eyes smiled at us, but when he was angry or upset, like now, they could cut us like knives. "Leah," he said, "what did you do to Mama's fish?"

"Please, Papa," I said, "don't let Mama kill our fish. His name is Joe. We love him. And we want to keep him for a pet."

"Where is he now?" Papa asked.

I looked down at my hands and began to pick my fingernail. I didn't want to tell Papa where Joe was. But he put his hand on my chin and forced my face up. "Where's the fish now?" he asked again. His voice was gentle. But those eyes were cutting me up.

"In Mrs. Ginzburg's bathtub," I mumbled.

Papa started walking again, faster now.

We trailed along behind him, not holding his hands anymore. He didn't say anything for a while. But when we got to our front stoop, he stopped to talk to us. "We are going to Mrs. Ginzburg's apartment. And we are getting that fish," he said. "It's your mother's fish. And it cost her a lot of money. She had to save a little out of what I give her each week just so she could buy such a big fish and make an extra nice Passover holiday for all of us." When we got to Mrs. Ginzburg's, Papa said to her, "We've come to take the fish home. I'm sorry for the trouble."

"Oh, he was no trouble," Mrs. Ginzburg said.

"Well, he would have been as soon as you wanted to take a bath," Papa said.

We didn't say anything.

Mrs. Ginzburg let the water out of the tub. Papa used his hands and the bucket to catch Joe.

It was much easier going back upstairs than it had been coming down. Papa carried the bucket. When we got into our apartment, I ran the water, and Papa poured Joe into our bathtub. Joe flitted so gaily through the water you'd think he was happy to be home. Foolish Joe.

"Carp are for eating," Papa said, "just like chicken. You always eat two helpings of chicken."

"We never met the chicken," I said.

Papa shook his head. "That's not the point, Leah," he said. "What was put on this earth to eat, we eat. We don't kill more creatures than we need, and we don't kill them for fun. But we eat what must be eaten. It would break your Mama's heart if she knew you children didn't like to eat her gefilte fish. We won't tell her about any of this. Mrs. Ginzburg won't tell her either."

So nobody told Mama about how we had stolen her carp. Luckily I was at school when she made Joe into gefilte fish. When I got home I asked Harry how he could have stood watching her catch Joe and carry him off into the kitchen.

"I didn't watch," Harry said. "When I saw her go to get Joe, I went right down to Mrs. Ginzburg's. But even there I could smell fish cooking."

Although Mama opened all the windows that afternoon and no one else seemed to notice anything, Harry and I thought we smelled fish cooking for days.

We cried ourselves to sleep that night and the next night, too. Then we made ourselves stop crying. After that, we felt as if we were twelve years older than Mama and Papa.

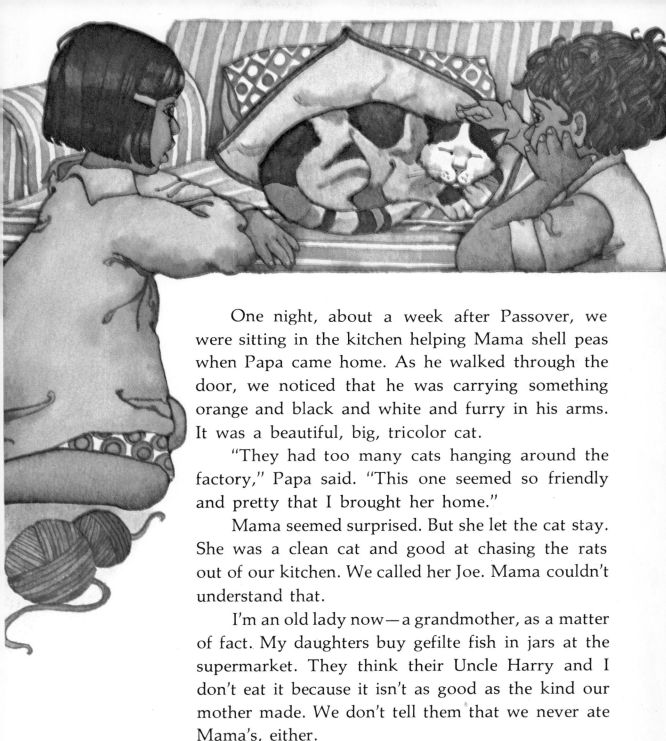

One night, about a week after Passover, we were sitting in the kitchen helping Mama shell peas when Papa came home. As he walked through the door, we noticed that he was carrying something orange and black and white and furry in his arms. It was a beautiful, big, tricolor cat.

"They had too many cats hanging around the factory," Papa said. "This one seemed so friendly and pretty that I brought her home."

Mama seemed surprised. But she let the cat stay. She was a clean cat and good at chasing the rats out of our kitchen. We called her Joe. Mama couldn't understand that.

I'm an old lady now—a grandmother, as a matter of fact. My daughters buy gefilte fish in jars at the supermarket. They think their Uncle Harry and I don't eat it because it isn't as good as the kind our mother made. We don't tell them that we never ate Mama's, either.

Robert Gray

food

Every living thing on earth—each plant and animal—needs other living things. Nothing lives alone. Sometimes the relationship is between parents and their young. Or often it is a group relationship, such as a family of monkeys. And sometimes the relationship is between the hunter and the hunted: he who eats and he who is eaten. For life survives by feeding on other life. This kind of a relationship is called a food chain. Some food chains are simple, others are complicated. All have this in common: They begin with the sun.

All life depends on energy from sunlight. Plants are the only living things that can use this energy directly. Their leaves are tiny factories that use sunlight to make food from water and minerals in the soil and carbon dioxide in the air. This process is called photosynthesis.

Plants, in turn, feed all other living things. Animals can only use the sun's life-giving energy after plants have changed it into food. Animals that feed on plants are called herbivores. When these animals are eaten

chains

by the carnivores—the meat eaters—the sun's energy is passed on again.

People are members of many food chains. One of the simplest is plant-to-human, which is when a person eats vegetables. When people eat meat or drink milk, they are part of a three-link chain: grass-to-cow-to-human.

One of the great things about any food chain is that it always produces enough for each of its members if it is left alone. There are more frogs and snakes and even baby hawks born than will live to become adults. Most become part of a food chain by being eaten before they grow up.

The sad fact is that people disturb and sometimes even destroy food chains. We spill oil and dump chemicals and wastes in the ocean and kill parts of food chains. We pollute rivers, lakes, and the air that are essential to all. In doing so, we may damage food chains we know little or nothing about. But this we do know: Each form of life is linked to all others. Breaking links puts all life in danger.

Here is an example
of a food chain:

1 A butterfly sips nectar from a flower. This nectar contains the sun's energy in the form of sugars made by the plant.

2 A dragonfly eats a butterfly.

3 It, in turn, is eaten by a frog.

4 The frog is caught by a watersnake.

5 The snake is snatched up by a red-shouldered hawk.

6 The hawk is called the final consumer because he is the last link in the chain. There is nothing that preys on him for food—while he is alive. But after he dies tiny organisms break down his body into its basic chemicals.

7 These chemicals are taken up by plant roots, and the food chain starts over again. So this chain of life is really a cycle, without beginning or ending.

Be a Word Scientist

Parts of words often contain clues that can help us understand the meaning of the whole word. For example, **herbivore** and **carnivore** both end in **vore**. **Vore** means "one that eats." **Herbi** means "plant." **Carni** means "flesh" or "meat." So a **herbivore** is "one that eats plants." And a **carnivore** is "one that eats meat." If **omni** means "all," what's an **omnivore?**

What do you think an **insectivore** is?

Now let's look at two more word parts that are often found in scientific words. **Ologist** means "specialist." **Ology** means "a branch of science." We all know that a zoo is a place where we can go to see living animals. But **zoo-** or **zo-** as part of a longer word means "animal." Now can you figure out what a **zoologist** is? A **zoologist** is "an animal specialist." And **zoology** is a branch of science that deals with animals. Here's another one. **Ec-** means "outside." So an **ecologist** is "an outside specialist." And **ecology** is "a branch of science that deals with the outside." Here are some more clues:

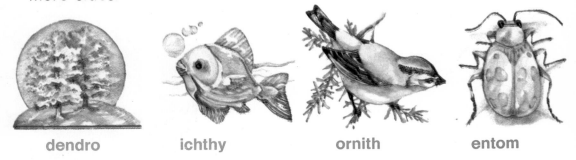

dendro   ichthy   ornith   entom

Now try being a word scientist and see if you can explain what the following words mean: dendrology, ichthyologist, entomologist, ornithologist.

What Will Happen to Pelicans?

Carole and Jim Hickman

Something is very wrong with pelicans these days. There are thousands of pelicans still on the earth. But soon there may be none. Pelicans have been on earth for 75 million years—since the time when the dinosaurs became extinct. Now pelicans are in danger of becoming extinct themselves.

The problem is with pelican eggs. Most pelicans alive today are grown-up. There are not many baby pelicans. The reason is that in the last ten years the big birds have been laying fewer and fewer eggs. And the shells of the pelican eggs are not as hard and strong as they used to be. Pelicans, like all birds, sit on their eggs until they hatch. But now many pelican eggs break when the parent sits on them. These eggs never hatch. If the eggs do not hatch, there can be no new pelicans.

Why has something gone wrong with pelican eggs? The answer has to do with people. And it has to do with the food that pelicans eat.

Pelicans are fishermen. A full-grown pelican eats about eight pounds of fish a day. You would have to eat thirty-two good-sized hamburgers a day to eat as much as a pelican does!

It is because of the fish they eat that pelicans are in trouble. You see, people have done something to the fish. Nobody meant to do anything to the fish. It was a mistake. It happened as people were trying to help other people.

In many places on the earth, certain insects have caused serious problems. Many, many people have died from insect bites. And insects have killed crops, so people have starved.

People wanted to do something about these harmful insects. They made a chemical called DDT. DDT has been sprayed all over the world in places where harmful insects lived. Many, many people and crops have been saved.

But people did not know that DDT does not go away

after it has been sprayed. Although it cannot be seen, DDT moves through air and water. DDT gets into all sorts of plants and animals. It becomes part of them.

In some places, there is a great amount of DDT in the water. It has become part of water plants. It has gotten into the bodies of many fish. Many fish eat water plants and smaller fish. The more a fish eats, the more DDT it has in its body.

Because pelicans eat so many fish, they have a great amount of DDT inside them. This DDT is very bad for the pelicans. It is the reason that they are laying fewer eggs. DDT is also the reason they are not laying eggs with good, strong shells. It is the reason that there may one day be no more pelicans.

Pelicans have been very helpful to people. Pelican waste makes very good

fertilizer for crops. This is one reason that it would be very sad for the pelicans to become extinct.

But there is another reason, too. Everything in nature has a place. When something happens to one animal or plant, it may affect another animal or plant. But it may take many years.

Pelicans like to eat a type of fish that most people don't like. There are enough of these fish now to feed the pelicans. But if all the pelicans die and nothing eats these fish, there may be more and more of them. If there are too many of these fish in the waters of the world, they may make something happen to some other kind of fish. We don't really know. But we do know that nothing happens in nature all by itself.

In some countries, people are no longer allowed to use DDT. But in other countries, DDT is still used. We hope that soon people everywhere will stop using DDT.

It will be very sad if pelicans become extinct. But if this happens, it will teach us an important lesson. It will teach us to be very careful about what we spray into the air and about what chemicals we use to make our lives better. It will teach us to save other animals from harm in the future.

WHAT CAN WE DO?

Alma Whitney

Some children in an elementary school in New York wanted to know if they could do anything to help animals that are in danger of becoming extinct.

The children went to the American Museum of Natural History to talk to Mr. Gene Agustin. Mr. Agustin is a zoologist, a scientist who studies animals.

"Before we talk about what you can do to help," Mr. Agustin said to the children, "let's try to understand some things about the problem. Do you know why many animals today are in danger of becoming extinct?" Some children said that they had learned DDT has hurt many animals. "You're right," said Mr. Agustin. "DDT and other things that harm animals are sometimes sprayed into the air."

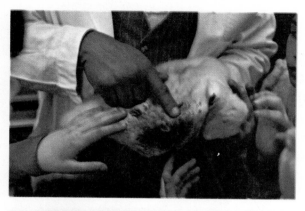

"There are other reasons that many animals are in danger of becoming extinct. Look at this. It's the skin of a baby seal. Can you see this ugly spot where the little seal was hit with a club?"

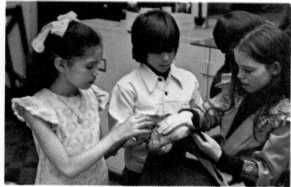

"Why would anyone want to club a little seal?"

Mr. Agustin explained that hunters club seals to death. Then the seal's fur is used to make coats. So many seals have been killed that now some kinds of seals are in danger of becoming extinct.

"It makes me sad to think about wearing the skin of a baby seal."

87

"Did any of you know that the tiger is also in danger of becoming extinct? People kill tigers for their skins. People will pay a lot of money for a coat or rug made out of tiger's skin."

"What's wrong with people, anyway?"

"I can see you're beginning to understand the problems," said Mr. Agustin. "But there's some good news about tigers. Most tigers live in India. The government of India has made it a crime to hunt tigers. The country has set aside special places where tigers can live safely. We don't know if this will keep the tigers from becoming extinct, but we hope it will. People have *got* to stop killing wild animals for their fur."

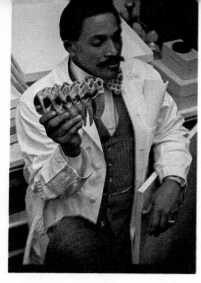

"This tooth comes from another animal in danger of becoming extinct—the Indian elephant."

"But why is the elephant in danger of becoming extinct? Elephants don't have fur."

"No, they don't," explained Mr. Agustin. "But some people kill elephants to get trophies or curios. For example, this is an elephant's foot someone made into an umbrella stand. People also kill elephants for their tusks. Some people feel very proud when they kill a really big animal."

"How could anyone be proud of killing an elephant?"

The children wanted to know if any animals had already been saved from becoming extinct. "We think so," Mr. Agustin told them. "In Ethiopia, for example, there is an animal called the oryx. It's a kind of antelope. People used to kill the oryx for its skin. Then, a few years ago, Ethiopia decided to try to save the oryx. The government sent some of them to the United States to see if a new herd could be formed. Now there is a small herd of oryx in Arizona. It is growing larger each year. So it looks like we may have saved the oryx. We will have to see how well they do in the next few years."

"Well, what can *we* do to save the animals? What *can* we do to help?"

"The first thing to do is learn all you can about the problems facing animals today," Mr. Agustin said. "Tell your families and friends what you learn. Join organizations which are trying to save the world's animals. And write letters to people in the government and tell them how you feel about animals being killed for no good reason."

91

On the way home,
the children discussed
what they might do
to help save the ani-
mals.

When they got back to school
they started telling their
friends about what they had
learned at the museum. They made posters about
animals in danger and hung them in the halls of the
school. They wrote articles for the school newspaper.
Then the children prepared an assembly program
about endangered animals. Here is part of a song
they wrote for the program.
You can sing it to the tune of "The Stars and
Stripes Forever."

We Are All in Danger

The tigers, the polar bears, too.
And maybe someday even you.
The dodos were here for so long.
But we no longer hear their song.
So let's give a big rousing cheer
For the animals that are still here.
We think that they are very dear.
And we don't want to see them all disappear.

GLOSSARY

This glossary will help you in pronouncing and understanding the meanings of unusual or difficult words in this book. If you need help in pronouncing the words, use the key at the bottom of each right-hand page.

ab·so·lute·ly (ab′ sə lo͞ot′lē, ab′ sə lo͞ot′ lē) completely; to the fullest extent or highest degree.

an·gle·worm (ang′gəl wurm′) a long worm that lives in the soil. This worm, also called an earthworm, is the most common worm that lives on earth.

an·nounced (ə nounst′) made known publicly or officially.

ant·eat·er (ant′ē′ tər) a toothless animal with a long sticky tongue that feeds on ants and termites.

an·ten·na (an ten′ ə) 1. the aerial of a radio or a television set. 2. the feeler, as on the head of an insect or lobster. *Antennae* is the plural form of antenna.

ap·pe·tite (ap′ ə tīt′) a desire for food; a craving.

beak (bēk) a bird's bill.

betch·a (bech′ ə) a slang word that stands for *I bet you.*

blood ves·sel (blud ves′əl) a type of tube in the body through which bloods flows.

brach·i·o·sau·rus (brak′ ē ō sôr′ əs) the heaviest of all dinosaurs. It was a plant-eater and lived in swamps.

bron·to·sau·rus (bron′ tə sôr′ əs) a plant-eating dinosaur which was one of the largest land animals, growing to a length of eighty feet and weighing up to thirty-five tons.

broth (brôth) a thin soup made by boiling meat, fish, or vegetables in water.

car·bon di·ox·ide (kär′bən dī ok′ sīd) a colorless, odorless gas made up of carbon and oxygen that is present in the atmosphere.

car·ni·vore (kär′ nə vôr′) any animal with long sharp teeth and claws that feeds on the flesh of other animals.

carp (kärp) 1. to find fault or complain. 2. a freshwater fish used as food.

chem·i·cal (kem′ i kəl) a substance made or used in *chemistry,* the science that deals with the characteristics of simple substances and the changes that take place when they react with other substances.

cli·mate (klī′ mit) the typical weather conditions of a particular place or region.

co·coon (kə ko͞on′) a case made of silk, leaves, or other materials that covers and protects the pupa of certain insects, while it develops into an adult.

com·plete (kəm plēt′) whole; entire.

com·pli·cat·ed (kom′ plə kā′ tid) hard to understand or do.

cone (kōn) 1. a fruit with scales that bear seeds, found on pine, cedar, fir, and other evergreen trees. 2. an object that narrows to a point from a round base.

con·sum·er (kən so͞o′ mər) someone who uses up things, such as food, services, or clothing.

at, āpe, fäther; end, mē; it, īce; odd, ōld, côffee; wood, fo͞ol; oil, out; up, ūse, turn; ə for *a* in *ago,* *e* in *taken,* *i* in *pencil,* *o* in *lemon,* *u* in *helpful;* **ch**in; sin**g**er; **th**in; **th**is; **zh**=**s** in treasure.

crack (krak) a break that does not cause separation into parts.

crea·ture (krē chər) any living being.

cush·ion (koosh' ən) a pillow or soft pad used to sit, rest, or lie on.

cy·cle (sī'kəl) 1. a series of events that happen over and over again in a definite order. 2. a period of time during which such a series occurs and completes itself. 3. a bicycle, tricycle, or motorcycle. 4. to ride a cycle.

def·i·nite·ly (def' ə nit lē) certainly.

de·liv·er·y (di liv' ər ē) carrying something to a particular place or person.

de·liv·er·y room (di liv'ər ē room) a room equipped to handle the birth of babies.

di·a·ry (dī' ər ē) a record written down every day, in which people tell what happened to them or what they thought that day.

din·o·saur (dī' nə sôr') a member of a large group of extinct reptiles that lived millions of years ago. Dinosaurs were of all sizes; some were the largest land animals that ever lived.

drag·on·fly (drag' ən flī) a slender-bodied flying insect found near fresh water which feeds on mosquitos and other insects.

e·col·o·gy (ē kol' ə jē) a study that deals with the relationships of living things and their surroundings.

e·nor·mous (i nôr' məs) much greater than normal in size, amount, or degree; extremely large.

en·vi·ron·men·tal (en vī' rən ment' əl) relating to the objects, influences, and conditions that surround and affect the development of an animal or plant.

ex·tinct (eks tingkt') no longer in existence; no longer active.

eye·drop·per (ī' drop' ər) a tube used for putting liquid medicine into the eye.

fer·ti·li·zer (furt' əl ī' zər) a substance, such as manure or certain chemicals added to the soil to make it richer or better able to produce healthy plants.

fes·ti·val (fes' tə vəl) a feast or holiday.

flit·ted (fli'təd) to move or pass swiftly or lightly; to dart.

foo·ey (foo'ē) a slang word used to express dislike of someone or something.

freak (frēk) a person, animal, or plant that has not developed normally.

ge·fil·te fish (gə fil' tə fish) chopped fish, usually a mixture of whitefish, pike, and carp that is mixed with chopped onion, egg, and so on, and boiled.

giz·zard (giz' ərd) the second part of a bird's stomach in which the food from the first stomach is finely ground.

gnat (nat) a small, winged insect that has sharp, biting mouth parts.

harm·ful (harm' fəl) causing or able to cause danger or damage.

her·bi·vore (hur' bə vôr') any animal that feeds mainly on plants.

hum·ming·bird (hum' ing burd') a small, brightly colored American bird which has a slender, pointed bill and narrow wings that beat very fast when it flies.

in mem·o·ry of (in mem'ər ē ov) an expression that means something done to remember someone or something.

in·tel·li·gent (in tel'ə jənt) having or showing knowledge or wisdom; bright.

in·ves·ti·gate (in ves' tə gāt') to look carefully at in order to uncover facts or get information.

jeep·ers (jēp'ərs) a slang word used to describe surprise at something.

kid (kid) 1. a young goat. 2. a young child. 3. to make fun of; to tease.

knife (nīf) 1. cutting tool having one or more sharp-edged blades. 2. the cutting blade of a tool or machine. *Knives* is the plural form of knife.

lar·va (lär′ və) the early wormlike stage of an insect after it hatches from an egg. *Larvae* is the plural form of larva.

let·tuce (le′ tis) a plant with green leaves that form a round, long, or oval head are usually eaten in salads.

li·brar·y (li′ brer′ē, li′ brər′ē) 1. a collection of books, records, pictures, or other reference materials. 2. a room or building holding such a collection.

lug (lug) 1. to pull or carry with effort. 2. a slang word for a clumsy or stupid person.

mam·mal (mam′ əl) a class of warm-blooded animals with backbones; the females of the species have milk glands to feed their young.

meas·ure·ment (mezh′ ər mənt) the size, amount, or quantity of something.

min·er·al (min′ ər əl) a substance which occurs in nature that is neither animal nor vegetable and has a characteristic chemical composition.

mor·sel (môr′ səl) a small bite or quantity of food.

mu·se·um (mū zē′ əm) a building or place where objects of value or interest in the fields of art, science, history, and so on are preserved and displayed.

my gosh (mī gosh) a slang expression used to show surprise or amazement.

nec·tar (nek′ tər) a sweet substance, especially the liquid formed in flowers and used by bees in making honey.

nurs·er·y (nur′ sər ē) 1. a room set apart for small children, especially a baby's bedroom. 2. a place where plants are raised for sale.

or·gan·ism (ôr′gə niz′ əm) a living animal or plant; any living thing.

or·gan·i·za·tion (ôr′ gə ni zā′ shən) 1. the act of putting things in order. 2. a group united for a particular purpose.

o·ryx (ôr′ iks) an antelope having a gray or brown coat with black or brown markings and long, nearly straight horns.

os·trich (ôs′trich, os′trich) a two-toed bird which has a long neck, long powerful legs, and a small white head. The male ostrich has large white plumes that are used for decoration. The ostrich is the largest of all birds. Athough it cannot fly, it can run very swiftly.

Pass·o·ver (pas′ ō vər) a Jewish holiday occurring in the spring, which celebrates the Jews' flight from Egypt.

peer (pēr) 1. to look closely in order to see clearly. 2. a person who is equal to another in age, ability, or social class.

pel·i·can (pel′ i kən) a web-footed water bird which has a large pouch beneath its bill that is used for storing fish.

pes·ti·cide (pes′ tə sīd′) a chemical used to destroy harmful plants or animals.

pho·to·syn·the·sis (fō′ tə sin′ thə sis) the process by which green plants make food.

pil·low·case (pi′ lō kās) a cover, usually made of cloth, for a pillow.

poi·so·nous (poi′ zə nəs) causing serious injury, illness, or death.

pol·lute (pə lōōt′) to make impure or dirty, as with harmful chemicals, gases, or other waste materials.

pouch (pouch) 1. a bag or sack. 2. a bag-like part of an animal's skin.

prey (prā) any animal that is hunted or killed by another animal for food.

proc·ess (pros′ əs, prō′ ses) the series of acts in making or doing something.

at, āpe, fäther; end, mē; it, īce; odd, ōld, côffee; wood, fool; oil, out; up, ūse, turn; ə for *a* in *ago*, *e* in *taken*, *i* in *pencil*, *o* in *lemon*, *u* in *helpful*; **ch**in; si**ng**er; **th**in; <u>**th**</u>is; **zh**＝**s** in treasure.

prog·ress (prog' res) a forward movement in space or toward a goal. (prə gres') to move forward and onward.

pu·pa (pū'pə) the stage of an insect's development after the larva stage and before the adult stage. A caterpillar in its cocoon is a *pupa*. *Pupae* is the plural form of pupa.

quar·ter (kwôr' tər) 1. one of four equal parts into which anything is or may be divided; one fourth. 2. a coin of the U.S. and Canada worth twenty-five cents.

ram (ram) 1. to hit against something with great force. 2. a male sheep.

rec·og·nize (rek' əg nīz) 1. to know again; to identify. 2. to see or understand clearly. 3. to take notice of; to admit.

re·la·tion·ship (ri lā' shən ship') the connection between two or more things.

scale (skāl) 1. a device used to weigh things. 2. a flat, hard plate which forms the outer covering, as of snakes or fish. 3. a series of steps or degrees, such as the scale of C major in music.

sci·ence (sī' əns) the body of knowledge which deals with things in nature and the universe and with the forces that create, shape, and form them.

sponge (spunj) 1. one of a group of animals that lives attached to rocks in or near water and which has a netlike structure. 2. the netlike skeleton of this animal, or anything like it, used for washing or to absorb liquid.

squat (skwot) 1. to sit with the knees bent and drawn close to or under the body. 2. to settle on land without having the right to do so.

squirm (skwurm) to turn or twist the body because of being uncomfortable.

starve (stärv) to suffer or die from hunger.

steg·o·sau·rus (steg' ə sôr' əs) a dinosaur that had a spiked tail and two rows of bony plates along its back.

sur·vive (sər vīv') to live longer than someone or something else; to outlive.

ten·ant (ten' ənt) a person who pays rent to live on the property of another.

thrash (thrash) to give a beating to something or someone.

tri·cer·a·tops (trī ser' ə tops') a plant-eating dinosaur that had one long horn over each eye, a shorter horn on the snout, and a bony shield coming out from the skull over the back of the neck.

tri·col·or (trī' kul' er) having three colors.

trow·el (trou'əl) a hand tool used for spreading and smoothing plaster or for scooping up earth.

tun·nel (tun' əl) a long, narrow passageway underground or underwater.

tusk (tusk) a long, pointed tooth, usually one of a pair, found in certain animals.

tweez·ers (twē'zərs) a small tool for plucking out hairs or for picking up tiny objects.

ty·ran·no·saur·us (ti ran' ə sôr' əs) a meat-eating dinosaur.

wob·ble (wob' əl) to move or sway unsteadily from side to side; to shake.

wring (ring) 1. to squeeze or press, especially so as to force out liquid. 2. to get by forceful or persistent effort.

wrin·kled (ring' kəld) having folds, lines, or creases.

yolk (yōk) the yellow part of an egg.

zo·ol·o·gist (zō ol' ə jist) an expert in the study of animal life.